I can do stories - Book 1

Written by
Sally Tears

Illustrated by
Jenn Garside

My heartfelt thanks to my wonderful illustrator Jenn Garside who has the incredible ability to bring my characters to life exactly as I visualized them.

My friend Angela Shepherd for her relentless grammar checks.

Finally my husband for his never ending belief in me.

I CAN DO STORIES

BOOK 1

Written by Sally Tears

Illustrated by Jenn Garside

SAMMY
THE SCARED
SEAGULL

It was so cosy and warm inside Sammy's egg, but he knew that today he would have to start pecking so that he could get out into the big wide world. He had heard his brothers and sisters pecking their way out all morning and knew it was time for him to do the same.

"Gosh! Where am I?" he said when he'd pecked his final peck.

"You're here in the nest with your brothers and sisters" said his Mum gently. "Welcome to the world".

Sammy didn't know if he liked this new world. It seemed rather cold and windy, not at all like his safe and warm world inside his egg.

"Now", said his Mum "I want you all to stay very still and wait for your Dad to return with some food. I am going to go and help him get enough for us all".

Off she flew and left Sammy with his brothers and sisters. There was a lot of pushing and shoving in the nest and all at once Sammy had been pushed right to the very edge.

"I wonder what I can see over the edge" he thought. He peered out "Oh dear, I'm so high up, I'll never be able to get down there, it's so far away. I hope I can stay here forever".

When his parents came home later with the food, Sammy told them how frightened he had been when he had looked over the edge.

"Don't worry sweetheart" his Mum had said. "When you grow up your Dad and I will teach you how to fly. It's really easy and then you will be able to fly down to the sea with everyone else".

Sammy spent most of the time as he was growing up in the centre of the nest. He didn't like it at all when his brothers and sisters pushed him near to the edge. It made him feel all wobbly and dizzy when he looked down.

One day his Dad returned to the nest and told everyone to practise flapping their wings.
"Why?" they asked eagerly.
"Because it is nearly time to start your flying lessons". He smiled. "And we need your wings to be really strong".

For the next few days everyone flapped and stretched their wings. Everyone except Sammy that is. The constant rocking movement made Sammy feel quite ill so he lay quietly in the middle of the nest and hoped that no one would notice him.

The great day arrived.
"Okay everyone" said Sammy's Dad. "All make your way to the edge of the nest and hold tightly with your feet". There was so much pushing and shoving that no one noticed that Sammy was still in the middle of the nest.

For hours they practised flapping their wings on the edge of the nest until their Dad decided that it was time to FLY!

One by one each of his brothers and sisters wobbled and swayed until one of them finally let go. He flapped his wings furiously and shouted "Hey look at me. I can fly".

One by one everyone took the plunge and started to fly. How excited they all were. All of them but Sammy. He lay quietly, hoping that no one would notice that he was still in the nest.

"Hello Sammy, what are you doing still here?" said his Dad. "Why aren't you out there flying with your brothers and sisters?"

"I'm too scared to go to the edge of the nest. It makes me feel wobbly and dizzy."

"Well, well, well" said his Dad. "I've never known a seagull to be scared of heights before. I'm not quite sure what to do about this. Don't worry, just wait there and I'll have a word with your Mum and see what we can do to make you feel better".

After a while his Dad came back smiling. "Okay Sammy, what I want you to do is jump on my back and hold tightly and Mum and I are going to take you down to the ground".

"I don't think I can do that. I will still feel all wobbly and dizzy when I look down" he whispered.

"Just hide your face in my feathers and you will be okay".

Off they set, Sammy snuggled into his Dad and his Mum flying behind to watch over him.

Before they knew it they had landed on the ground. "Off you get Sammy" said his Dad and Sammy slid very slowly on to the sand. He looked up to where the nest was and said "I'll never get back up there".

His Dad laughed "Not today Sammy but one day you will. Now what I want you to do is stand on the ground and flap your wings".

Sammy stood and for the first time actually flapped his wings. What fun it was. His wings made a funny fluttering noise that made him laugh. He practised for ages.

"That's enough for today Sammy" said his Dad. "Now hop on my back and we will all go back home".

Sammy slept really well that night and couldn't wait for tomorrow so that he could practise again.

Every day his parents took him down to the floor and he practised flapping his wings. After a few days his Dad put him on a pebble to practise on and the next day a small rock. Each day his Dad would put him on a larger and larger rock and say "Flap your wings and jump Sammy".

"I can nearly fly, I can nearly fly" he said one day when he had jumped from a really large rock.

The next day Sammy hopped on his Dad's back as usual to go to the ground but guess what happened?

Sammy didn't hide his head under his Dad's wings. Instead he looked up, and around, and down and guess what? He didn't feel all wobbly and dizzy. He felt WONDERFUL!

And guess what?

The next day ...
HE COULD FLY !

THE WAVE THAT WAVED

"I'm so bored crashing against this rock" sighed the Little Wave. "There must be something more interesting for me to do."

"Why don't you go to the beach and play with the children?" said one of the older waves. "You might have more fun there."

"What is a beach? What are children?" asked the Little Wave excitedly.

"Well a beach is a lot of sand without waves all over it, and children like to play on the beach with their buckets and spades. It's great fun to try and tickle their toes when they are paddling or collecting water in their buckets"

"Oh it sounds like great fun. Please will you take me there?"

Off they went, the Little Wave getting more and more excited the nearer they got.

"Show me what to do. Show me what to do!" shouted the Little Wave when they arrived.

"Okay" said the Big Wave. "Can you see that little girl there, the one that is dipping her toes in the water? Just dash up to her and tickle them."

The Little Wave dashed up to the little girl and ran all over her feet. The little girl laughed and laughed so he did it again and again. It was just the best fun. "This is better than banging on rocks all day" he thought.

The Little Wave played with the children all day. He filled buckets and tickled lots of toes and sometimes he got water on their clothes (I don't think he was supposed to do that do you?) He was just happy.

At the end of the day the children started to collect their things and get ready for home.

As they were leaving the beach they turned to the Little Wave and said "Goodbye Little Wave see you tomorrow".

And then guess what they did? They waved goodbye.

"What are they doing?" the Little Wave asked.
"Why, they are waving" smiled the Big Wave.
"But I'm a wave and I can't wave" sighed the Little Wave.
"Well you need to practise" said the Big Wave.

All through the night the Little Wave practised and practised until he fell asleep exhausted.
He woke up the next morning and dashed to the beach to wait for the children.

What great fun he had all day with them. They all laughed and laughed. He splashed and tickled and they jumped and giggled. All too soon it was time to go home. The children and waved goodbye.
"See you tomorrow" they said.

"Wait! Wait!" shouted Little Wave and guess what happened... He jumped out of the water – made the white froth into the shape of a hand and the Little Wave.... WAVED!

I wonder who the Little Wave will wave to next?

OLLY
THE
OCTOPUS

THE PROBLEMS WITH BS AND DS

Olly the Octopus is quite a sight – with his huge red hat, blue body and long magic legs that can do almost anything. When Olly is trying to solve a problem he sometimes scratches his nose with one of his feather dusters and then – watch out – all sorts of strange and wonderful things can happen!

I wonder if he'll scratch his nose in this story?

I know you are waiting for the story to begin – so are you sitting comfortably?
Well then let's begin.

This magical adventure started with a little boy called James.

James was an ordinary little boy with a happy family, but he was worried about one thing – he couldn't read very well. He tried very hard, but he didn't seem to be as good as his friends.

Can you remember when you started to read? It seemed very difficult didn't it? I bet some of you are still finding it hard. Well, don't worry, because Olly can help you, just like he helped James.

James was lying in bed one night worrying about his 'ABCs. He'd tried so hard that night to say them with his mum but he'd got so many Bs and Ds wrong that he couldn't get to sleep for worrying. He closed his eyes tight shut and pretended he was asleep.

Guess what happened next?

All of a sudden he opened his eyes. He didn't see his bedroom, he saw the most beautiful place, it was a land of beautiful colours and James knew it was a happy place to be.

He looked around to see where he was and that was when he saw Olly. He wasn't frightened by Olly, he was fascinated. Olly had the kindest face, he smiled and his eyes twinkled. James loved Olly's top hat and the hair that sprang out at the sides.

"Where am I?" asked James.

"Welcome to Never Worry Land" said Olly, with a voice that sounded soft like raindrops.

"How did I get here?" asked James.

"By magic" Olly laughed.

"But magic doesn't exist any more" said James.

"Oh really? I must remember that" said Olly.

"Who are you and where is Never Worry Land?"

"My name is Olly, and Never Worry Land is a magic land where we want to help all children who are worried. Why are you worried James?

"I was in bed worrying about my Bs and Ds and when I opened my eyes I was here".
"Let me show you around" smiled Olly. "Hold on to one of my tentacles and I'll take you".

James took hold of one of Olly's tentacles and off they went. James was very happy. He started to smile – he wasn't worried any more. Do you know why?

Well I told you earlier that each of Olly's arms could do something different and James was holding the 'smile' arm.

They walked down an amazing road. It was made of different coloured stones. The buildings were all brightly coloured with pretty gardens. There were animals everywhere.

"Let me take you to squirrel school to see if they can help you", Olly said "You see the squirrels make the shapes of the letters with their big furry tails. But before you can know your Bs from your Ds you need to know your right from your left."

"That's another problem" said James. "I can't remember that either".

"Oh, that's easy to learn" smiled Olly. "Which hand do you draw with?"

"This one" said James, holding up his right hand.

"So when you get older you'll write with your right hand", said Olly "You'll always know your right hand from your left hand by remembering that you write with your right hand, so your other hand must be your left. Simple isn't it?"

"Like Bs and Ds" said James excitedly, "but I still don't know which are which!"

"That's where the left and the right come in" said Olly. "Look at the squirrel who's looking to the right – his tail is drawn behind him – he is a 'd' shape. The squirrel who is looking to the left is bringing his tail behind him – he's a 'b' shape".

23

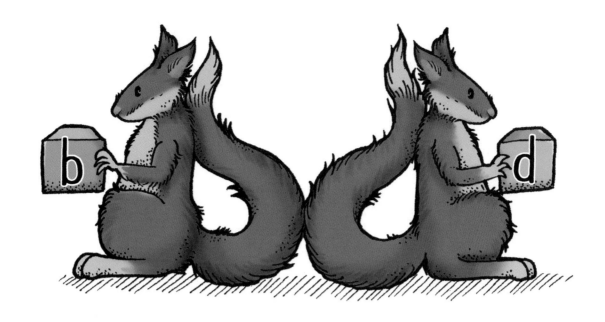

James and Olly played for a long time with the squirrels making B and D shapes until James didn't even have to think about left or right, he could remember the shapes correctly.

"It's time to go home now James" said Olly. "I hope you have enjoyed your adventure in Never Worry Land".

"Oh yes thank you Olly. I'm glad you taught me so much. I won't worry again, because I know that all problems can be solved" said James.

"I'm so glad" said Olly. "Worrying wastes such a lot of time".

Then guess what happened?

Olly was so happy that he had helped James that

he got quite excited and began to jump up and down and when Olly gets excited all sorts of things can happen.

"Oh, oh" laughed Olly "Watch out". I've just tickled my nose with my feather dusters".

James couldn't believe his eyes. Olly's hat fell off and three rabbits jumped out, closely followed by two doves and a ferret! Bunches of flowers leapt out of his pocket and suddenly a host of beautiful butterflies filled the sky.
"Now that's magic" laughed Olly rescuing his hat and popping it back on his head.

James rubbed his eyes. He was back in his bedroom. His Mum was standing by his bed. "Come on sleepy head" she said "wake up, it's time to get up".

James looked at the 'ABC' letters in his play box. He leapt out of bed and tipped them on to the floor. He rummaged through them and triumphantly pulled out a 'b' and 'd'. He imagined they were squirrels.

"Look Mum, This is a, 'b' and this is a 'd'!" James exclaimed.

"Well done James. How did you learn to do that? You can't have learnt it in your sleep" said his Mum.

"By MAGIC!" laughed James.

I wonder what magical adventure Olly will have next and will he scratch his nose with his feather dusters?

About the Author - Sally Tears

Many, many years ago I was fortunate enough to have not only been born in Yorkshire (UK) but into the most amazing family who taught me that if you wanted something then with hard work and belief you could have it. I have been able to achieve so many wonderful things in my life just by following what really is a simple premise but more importantly I have also been able to help many others to become successful and follow their dreams.

I started my career as a professional singer aged 16 with an all girl band called The Ivy Benson Band. We brought out a pop group from within the band called Sally and the Alley Cats (long before the Spice Girls were probably born). We made records, videos, did TV etc. But then I met the man of my dreams and became a wife and mother.

I loved the idea that performing builds such confidence in young people, so much so that I also started a part time business teaching speech and drama leading to LAMDA qualifications.

Working with young people is so inspirational, helping them develop not only their confidence but their imagination and that led to me writing stories and plays.

I really hope that you enjoy my stories and if you would like Olly to solve other problems that keep you awake then contact me on my Facebook page.
Facebook.com/sallytears1

Printed in Poland
by Amazon Fulfillment
Poland Sp. z o.o., Wrocław